Theory Paper Grade 3   2005   A

Duration 1¹/₂ hours

Candidates should answer ALL questions.
Write your answers on this paper — no others will be accepted.
Answers must be written clearly and neatly — otherwise marks may be lost.

1 Add the missing bar-lines to these three melodies, which all begin on the first beat of the bar.

 10

MacDowell

D. Scarlatti

Anon.

etc.

2 Add the correct rest(s) at the places marked * to make each bar complete.

 10

Musorgsky

3

3 Transpose this melody *down* an octave, using the bass clef as shown.

10

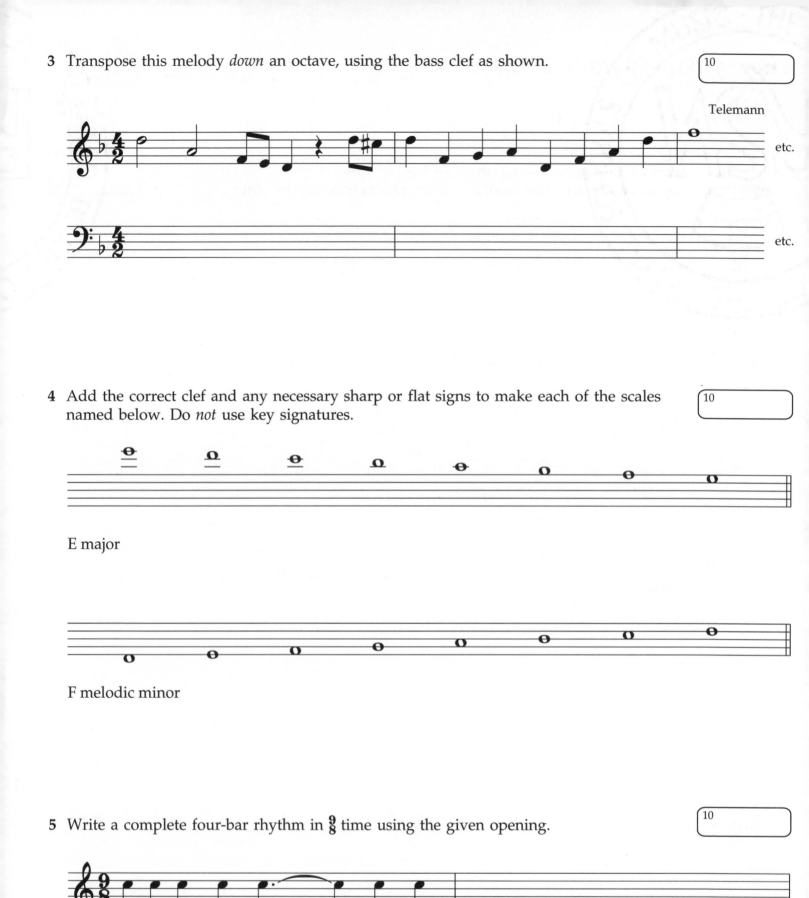

4 Add the correct clef and any necessary sharp or flat signs to make each of the scales named below. Do *not* use key signatures.

10

E major

F melodic minor

5 Write a complete four-bar rhythm in 9/8 time using the given opening.

10

6 Describe each of these melodic intervals, giving the type and number (e.g. major 3rd, perfect 8ve). The keys are named, and in each case the lower note is the key note. `[10]`

Bb major

F# minor

Ab major

Type ....

Type ....

Type ....

Number ....

Number ....

Number ....

D major

G minor

Type ....

Type ....

Number ....

Number ....

7 The following passage from a piano piece by Reinecke contains *five* deliberate mistakes. Rewrite it correctly on the given stave. `[10]`

5

8 This melody is from a piano piece by Diabelli. Look at it and then answer the questions below.

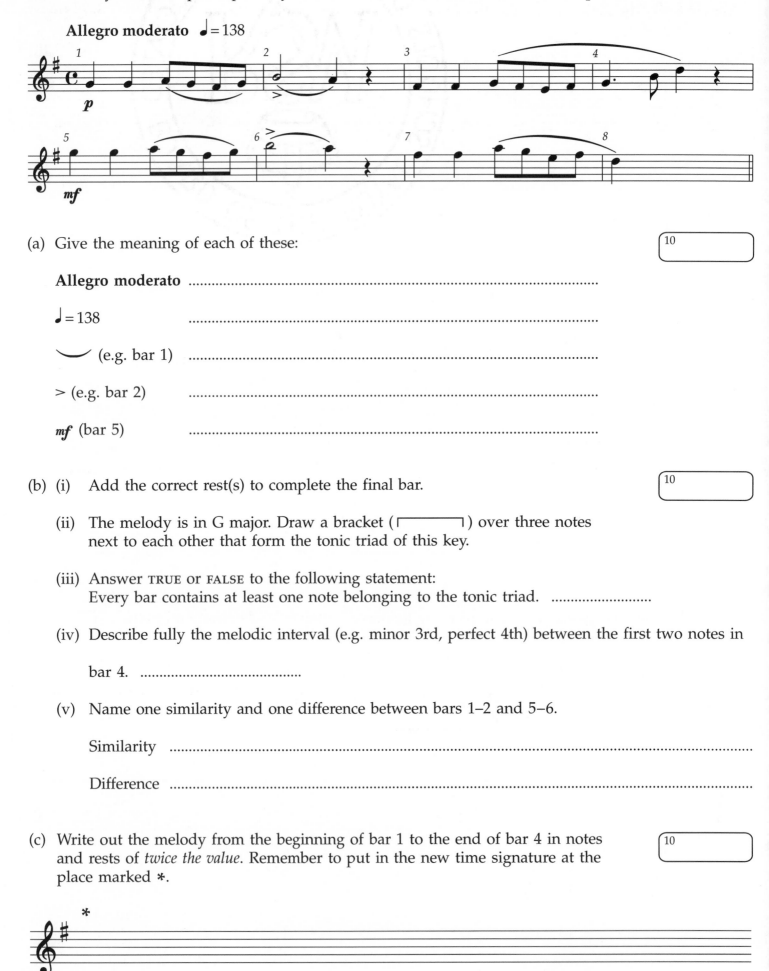

(a) Give the meaning of each of these: `10`

   Allegro moderato ....

   ♩ = 138 ....

   ⌣ (e.g. bar 1) ....

   > (e.g. bar 2) ....

   mf (bar 5) ....

(b) (i) Add the correct rest(s) to complete the final bar.   `10`

   (ii) The melody is in G major. Draw a bracket (⌐‾‾‾¬) over three notes
         next to each other that form the tonic triad of this key.

   (iii) Answer TRUE or FALSE to the following statement:
         Every bar contains at least one note belonging to the tonic triad. ....

   (iv) Describe fully the melodic interval (e.g. minor 3rd, perfect 4th) between the first two notes in

         bar 4. ....

   (v) Name one similarity and one difference between bars 1–2 and 5–6.

         Similarity ....

         Difference ....

(c) Write out the melody from the beginning of bar 1 to the end of bar 4 in notes   `10`
    and rests of *twice the value*. Remember to put in the new time signature at the
    place marked *∗*.

6

Theory Paper Grade 3   2005   B

Duration 1$^1/_2$ hours

TOTAL MARKS
100

Candidates should answer ALL questions.
Write your answers on this paper — no others will be accepted.
Answers must be written clearly and neatly — otherwise marks may be lost.

1 Add the time signature to each of these five melodies.

10

Karganov

Hook

etc.

Cui

Schumann

etc.

Telemann

2 Write a complete four-bar rhythm in $\frac{6}{8}$ time using the given opening.
   Note that this begins on an upbeat, and remember to complete the first whole bar.

10

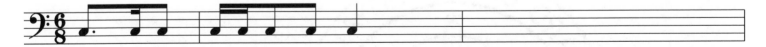

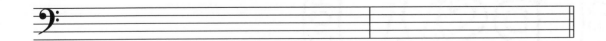

3 Write as semibreves (whole-notes) the scales named below.

C♯ melodic minor, ascending, with key signature.

A♭ major, descending, without key signature but including any necessary sharp or flat signs.

4 *After* each of these notes write a higher note to form the named *melodic* interval. The key is F♯ minor.

10

perfect 4th

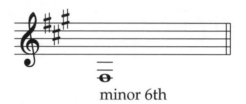
minor 6th

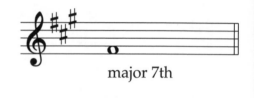
major 7th

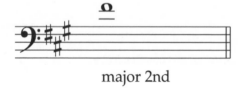
major 2nd

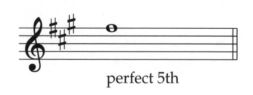
perfect 5th

10

5 (a) Rewrite the following with the notes correctly grouped (beamed).

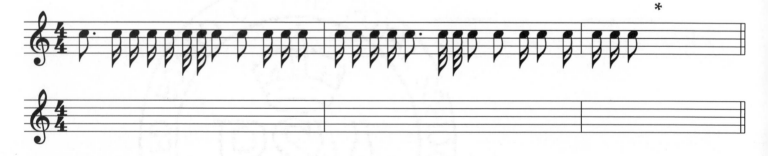

(b) Add the correct rest(s) at the place marked ✳ to complete the final bar.

6 Add the correct clef and any necessary sharp or flat signs to each of these tonic triads.
Do *not* use key signatures.

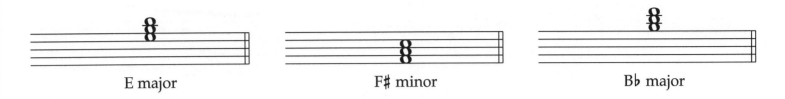

E major   F♯ minor   B♭ major

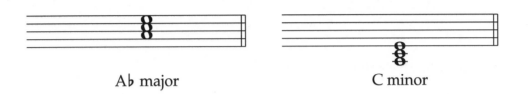

A♭ major   C minor

7 (a) The following passage from a piano piece by Karganov contains *four* deliberate
   mistakes. Rewrite it correctly on the given stave.

   (b) Give the letter name of the *highest* note of the extract. ....

8 This melody is from a minuet by J. S. Bach. Look at it and then answer the questions below.

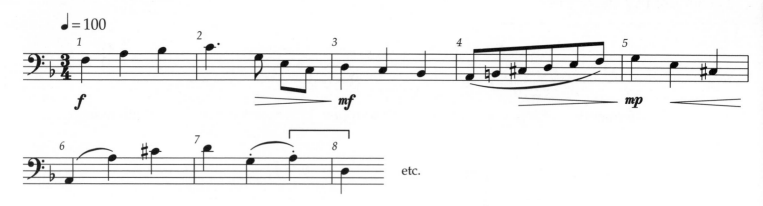

(a) Give the meaning of each of these:

♩= 100 ....

⸺⸺ (e.g. bar 4) ....

mp (bar 5) ....

⌒ (e.g. bar 6) ....

⌒· (bar 7) ....

(b) (i) Describe the time signature as: simple or compound ....

duple, triple or quadruple ....

(ii) Name a key in which all the notes of bar 4 can be found. ....

(iii) Which bar contains two notes next to each other that are an octave apart? Bar ....

(iv) How many demisemiquavers (32nd-notes) is the first note of bar 2 worth? ....

(v) Describe fully the melodic interval (e.g. major 3rd, perfect 4th)
between the two notes marked with a bracket () in bars 7–8. ....

(c) Write out the melody from the beginning of bar 1 to the end of bar 4
an octave higher, using the treble clef as shown.

Theory Paper Grade 3   2005   C

Duration 1¹/₂ hours

Candidates should answer ALL questions.
Write your answers on this paper — no others will be accepted.
Answers must be written clearly and neatly — otherwise marks may be lost.

TOTAL MARKS
100

10

1 Transpose this melody *down* an octave, using the bass clef as shown.

J. S. Bach

10

2 Write a complete four-bar rhythm in ³⁄₂ time using the given opening.
Note that this begins on an upbeat, and remember to complete the first whole bar.

10

3 Add the correct rest(s) at the places marked ✱ to make each bar complete.

4 (a) Rewrite the following with the notes correctly grouped (beamed).

Handel

(b) This melody is in G minor. Which other key has the same key signature? ....

5 Name the key of each of the following scales. Where the key is minor, state whether the scale is in the harmonic or melodic form.

Key ....

Key ....

Key ....

Key ....

6 Write the key signature and tonic triad of each of these keys.

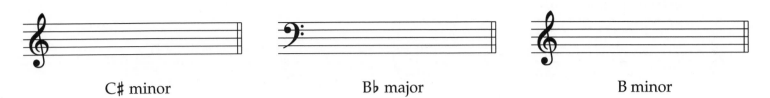

C♯ minor   B♭ major   B minor

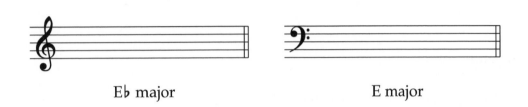

Eb major   E major

7 *After* each of these notes write a higher note to form the named *melodic* interval. The key is F minor.

major 7th   minor 6th   perfect 5th

major 2nd   perfect 4th

8 This violin melody is from a string quartet by Haydn. Look at it and then answer the questions below.

Poco adagio; cantabile

(a) Give the meaning of each of these:

Poco ....

adagio ....

cantabile ....

dolce ....

⌢• (bar 8) ....

(b) (i) Complete this sentence: The music begins in the key of
G major, but the C♯ in bar 7 suggests that it ends in the key of .... major.

(ii) Draw a circle round three notes next to each other that form the tonic triad
of the key you named in (i).

(iii) Answer TRUE or FALSE to this statement:
The time signature ¢ means that there are two minim (half-note) beats in a bar. ....

(iv) How many demisemiquavers (32nd-notes) is the first note of bar 4 worth? ....

(v) The first phrase has been marked with a bracket (⌐‾‾‾‾‾‾‾‾¬).
Mark the other phrases in the same way.

(c) Write out the melody from the beginning of the music to the first note of bar 4 in
notes of *half the value*. Remember to put in the new time signature at the place
marked *.

Theory Paper Grade 3   2005   S

Duration 1¹/₂ hours

Candidates should answer ALL questions.
Write your answers on this paper — no others will be accepted.
Answers must be written clearly and neatly — otherwise marks may be lost.

10

1   Add the time signature to each of these five melodies.

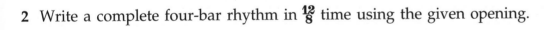

10

2   Write a complete four-bar rhythm in $\frac{12}{8}$ time using the given opening.

3 *After* each of these notes write a higher note to form the named *melodic* interval. The key is G minor.

perfect 5th

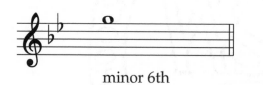

minor 6th

minor 3rd

major 7th

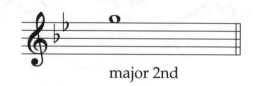

major 2nd

4 Rewrite the following with the notes correctly grouped (beamed).

5 Write as semibreves (whole-notes) the scales named below.

F♯ melodic minor, descending, with key signature.

E♭ major, ascending, without key signature but including any necessary sharp or flat signs.

6 Transpose this melody *up* an octave, using the treble clef as shown.

7 Add the correct clef and any necessary sharp or flat signs to each of these tonic triads. 10
  Do *not* use key signatures.

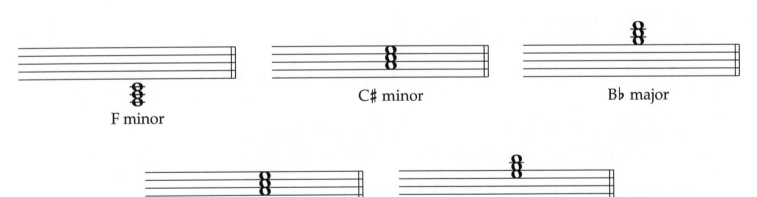

8 This melody is from a piano piece by Grieg. Look at it and then answer the questions below.

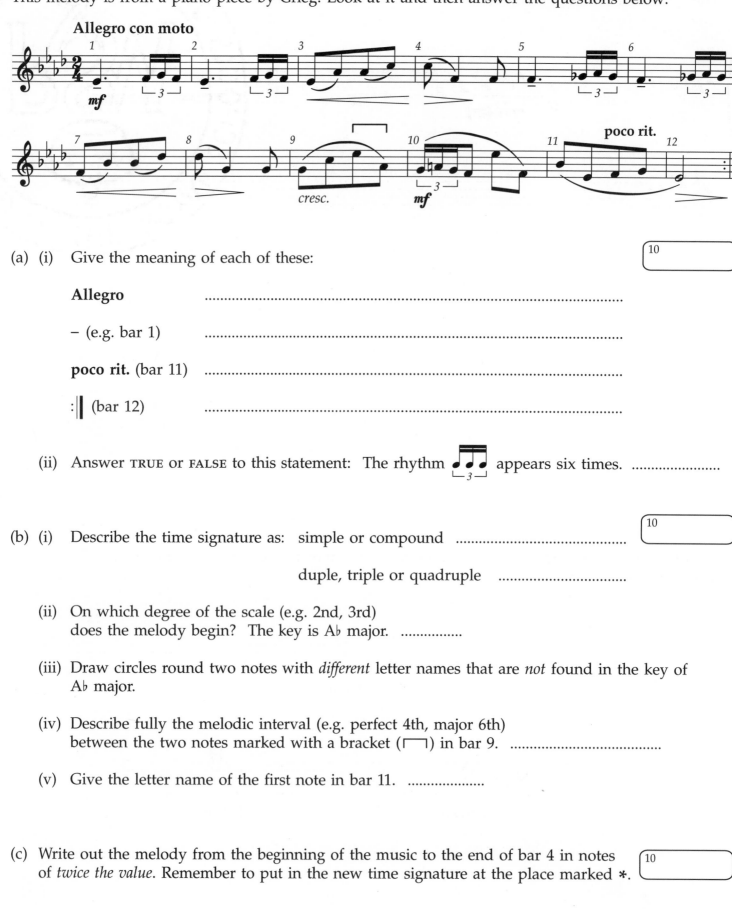

(a) (i) Give the meaning of each of these:

    Allegro ....

    – (e.g. bar 1) ....

    poco rit. (bar 11) ....

    :‖ (bar 12) ....

10

(ii) Answer TRUE or FALSE to this statement: The rhythm ♩♪♪ appears six times. ....

(b) (i) Describe the time signature as: simple or compound ....

10

                                 duple, triple or quadruple ....

(ii) On which degree of the scale (e.g. 2nd, 3rd)
does the melody begin? The key is A♭ major. ....

(iii) Draw circles round two notes with *different* letter names that are *not* found in the key of
A♭ major.

(iv) Describe fully the melodic interval (e.g. perfect 4th, major 6th)
between the two notes marked with a bracket (⌐⌐) in bar 9. ....

(v) Give the letter name of the first note in bar 11. ....

(c) Write out the melody from the beginning of the music to the end of bar 4 in notes
of *twice the value*. Remember to put in the new time signature at the place marked *.

10